By
Anthony Tallarico

Copyright © 1992 Kidsbooks, Inc. and Anthony Tallarico
7004 N. California Avenue
Chicago, IL 60645

ISBN: 0-8317-4981-4

This edition published in 1992 by SMITHMARK Publishers, Inc.,
16 East 32nd Street, New York, N.Y. 10016

SMITHMARK books are available for bulk purchase for sales promotion and premium use.
For details write or telephone the Manager of Special Sales, SMITHMARK Publishers, Inc.,
16 East 32nd Street, New York, N.Y. 10016   (212) 532-6600

Manufactured in the United States of America

HOT-AIR BALLOON

A hot-air balloon achieves flight when the air inside the balloon is heated. Since the heated air inside is lighter than the cool air outside, the balloon rises toward the sky.

The first hot-air balloon to carry passengers was invented by the Montgolfier brothers in France in 1783. It flew about 5 miles.

See if you can find all the things you did or didn't know about hot-air balloons in this picture. Don't forget to look for the following fun things, too.

☐ Arrows (7)
☐ Bee
☐ Cactus
☐ Candle
☐ Carrot
☐ Dragon
☐ Duck
☐ Eye
☐ Fire hydrant
☐ First passenger balloon
☐ Fish
☐ Flowers
☐ Football
☐ Happy face
☐ Heart
☐ Humpty Dumpty
☐ Ice-cream cone
☐ Kite
☐ Light bulb
☐ Lips
☐ Moon face
☐ Paper airplane
☐ Pencil
☐ Star
☐ Superhero
☐ Teapot
☐ Tent
☐ Thermometer
☐ Top hat
☐ Umbrella

What is another name for the balloon?
How can the balloon move downward at a faster speed?

LIGHT BULB

An electric light bulb contains a filament, an inert gas, electrical contacts, and a glass bulb. Light is produced when an electric current passes through the filament. The current heats the filament to a temperature high enough to produce white light.

Thomas Edison invented the light bulb in 1879.

See if you can find all the things you did or didn't know about light bulbs in this picture. Don't forget to look for the following fun things, too.

- ☐ Alarm clock
- ☐ Apple
- ☐ Baby's bib
- ☐ Baseball bat
- ☐ Bone
- ☐ Burned-out bulb
- ☐ Candles (2)
- ☐ Clipboard
- ☐ Clown
- ☐ Crayon
- ☐ Elephant
- ☐ Envelope
- ☐ Fish (2)
- ☐ Flowers (2)
- ☐ Football
- ☐ Fork
- ☐ Ghost
- ☐ Heart
- ☐ Helmet
- ☐ Horse's head
- ☐ Horseshoe
- ☐ Hose
- ☐ Jump rope
- ☐ Necktie
- ☐ Paintbrush
- ☐ Paper bag
- ☐ Pencil
- ☐ Pizza box
- ☐ Saw
- ☐ Tepee
- ☐ Used tire
- ☐ Vest

What is a filament made of? What determines the brightness of a light bulb?

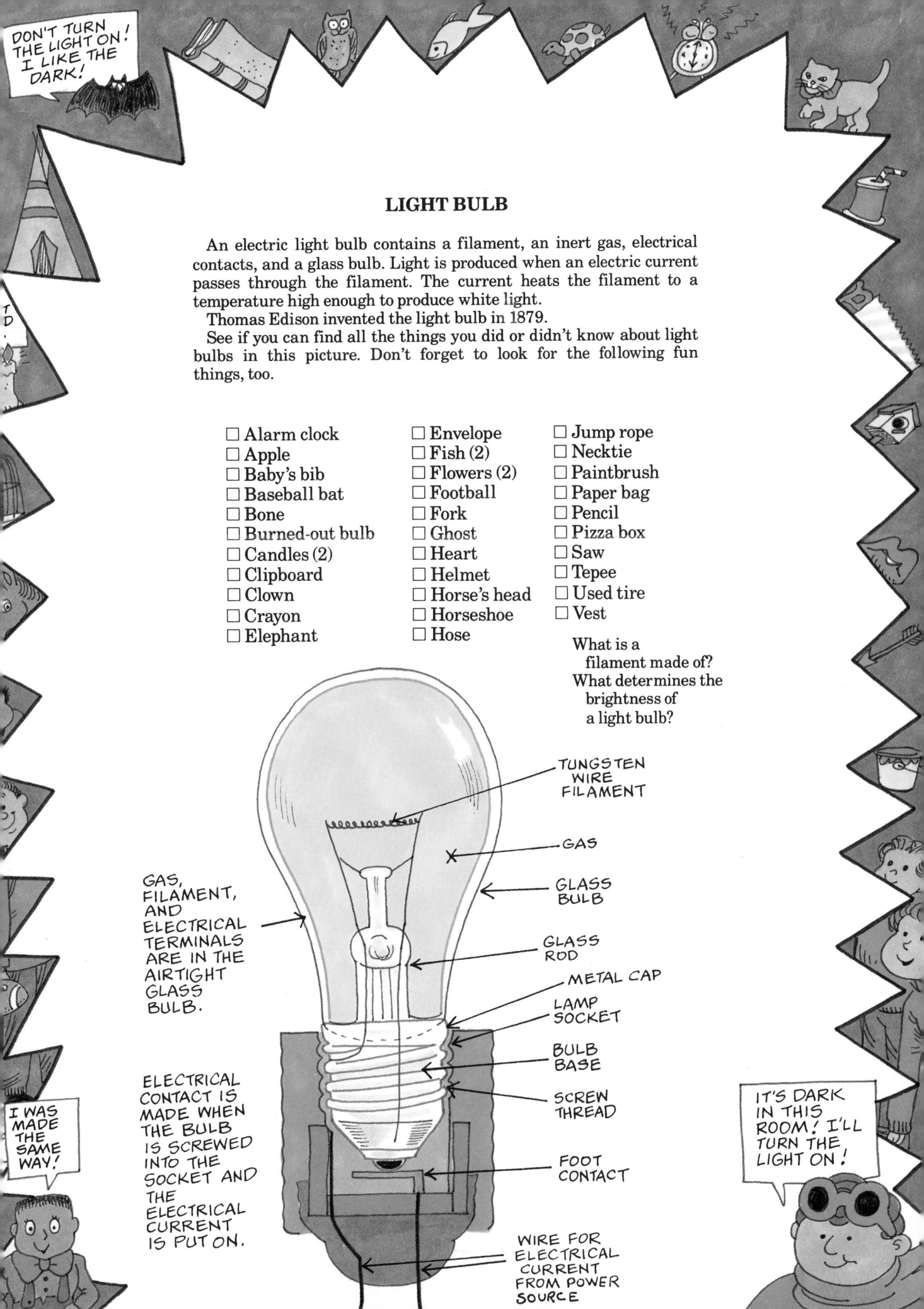

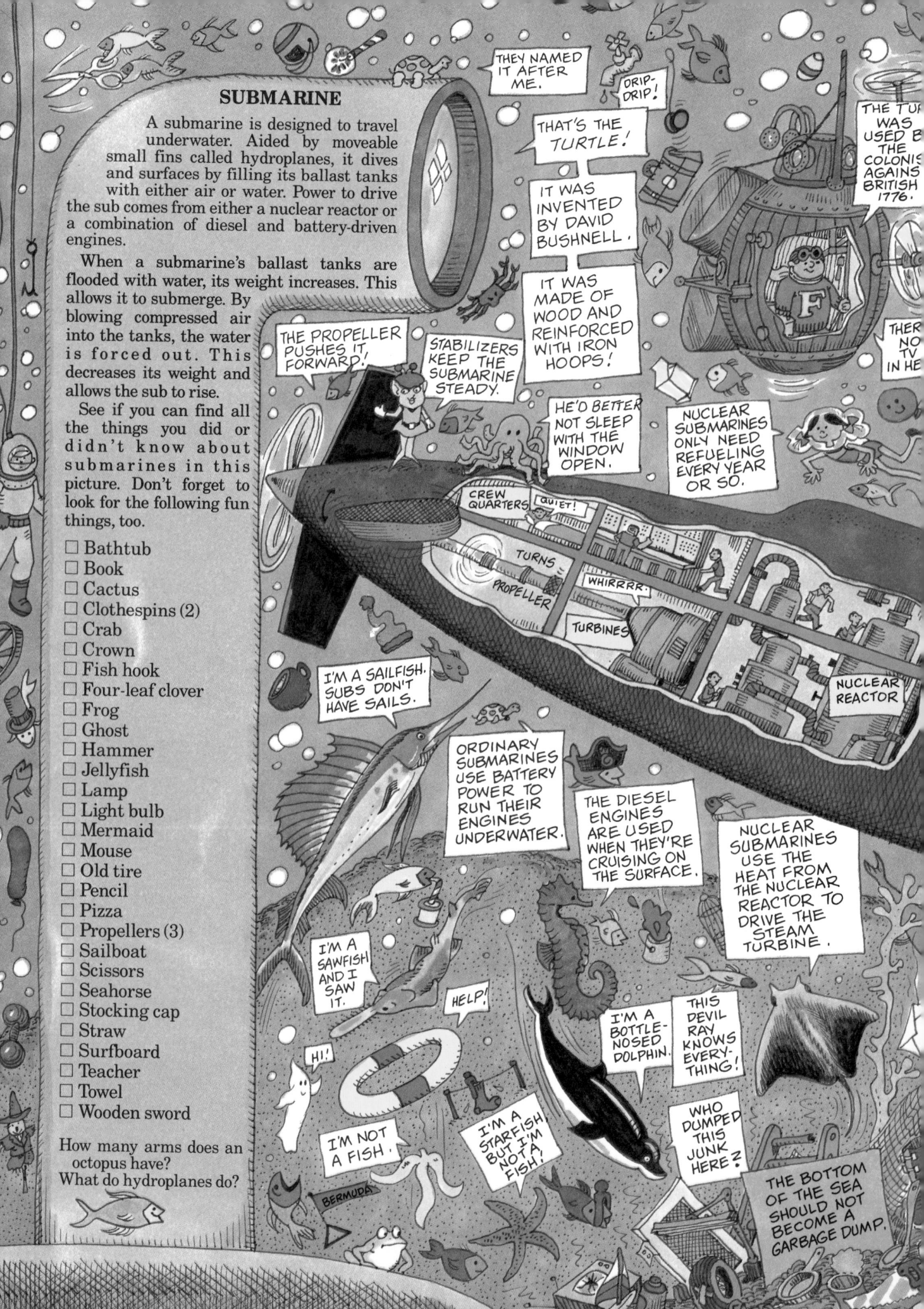

SUBMARINE

A submarine is designed to travel underwater. Aided by moveable small fins called hydroplanes, it dives and surfaces by filling its ballast tanks with either air or water. Power to drive the sub comes from either a nuclear reactor or a combination of diesel and battery-driven engines.

When a submarine's ballast tanks are flooded with water, its weight increases. This allows it to submerge. By blowing compressed air into the tanks, the water is forced out. This decreases its weight and allows the sub to rise.

See if you can find all the things you did or didn't know about submarines in this picture. Don't forget to look for the following fun things, too.

- ☐ Bathtub
- ☐ Book
- ☐ Cactus
- ☐ Clothespins (2)
- ☐ Crab
- ☐ Crown
- ☐ Fish hook
- ☐ Four-leaf clover
- ☐ Frog
- ☐ Ghost
- ☐ Hammer
- ☐ Jellyfish
- ☐ Lamp
- ☐ Light bulb
- ☐ Mermaid
- ☐ Mouse
- ☐ Old tire
- ☐ Pencil
- ☐ Pizza
- ☐ Propellers (3)
- ☐ Sailboat
- ☐ Scissors
- ☐ Seahorse
- ☐ Stocking cap
- ☐ Straw
- ☐ Surfboard
- ☐ Teacher
- ☐ Towel
- ☐ Wooden sword

How many arms does an octopus have?
What do hydroplanes do?

MAKING PAPER

About 5,000 years ago, the Egyptians used a writing material made from a plant called papyrus. Today, from soft tissues to tough cardboard, paper is made chiefly from fibers produced by trees, in large factories called paper mills.

See if you can find all the things you did or didn't know about making paper in this picture. Don't forget to look for the following fun things, too.

- ☐ Balloon
- ☐ Basket
- ☐ Bear
- ☐ Bird
- ☐ Bow and arrow
- ☐ Broom
- ☐ Bucket
- ☐ Cane
- ☐ Carrot
- ☐ Fish
- ☐ Flower
- ☐ Fork
- ☐ Heart
- ☐ Ice-cream cone
- ☐ Key
- ☐ Kite
- ☐ Mouse
- ☐ Mushroom
- ☐ Oilcan
- ☐ Owl
- ☐ Paper airplane
- ☐ Plumber's helper
- ☐ Ring
- ☐ Shopping bag
- ☐ Skier
- ☐ Snowman
- ☐ Telescope
- ☐ Toothbrush
- ☐ Turtles (2)
- ☐ Wizard
- ☐ Worm

What are calendar stacks?
Who invented the kind of paper that we use today?

HELICOPTER

Helicopters can fly straight up or down, forward or backward, sideways, and even hover in place. Because of their mobility they can fly into places that airplanes cannot.

The first helicopter to achieve flight was built in France in 1907. But it was not completely reliable. In 1939, Igor Sikorsky developed the first successful one and the modern era of helicopters began.

See if you can find all the things you did or didn't know about helicopters in this picture. Don't forget to look for the following fun things, too.

- ☐ Balloon
- ☐ Bee
- ☐ Book
- ☐ Butterfly
- ☐ Cactus
- ☐ Camera
- ☐ Candy cane
- ☐ Canteen
- ☐ Flying bat
- ☐ Frog
- ☐ Heart
- ☐ Jack-o'-lantern
- ☐ Lollipop
- ☐ Medal
- ☐ Mouse
- ☐ Oilcan
- ☐ Owl
- ☐ Pail
- ☐ Paper airplane
- ☐ Penguin
- ☐ Periscope
- ☐ Roller skates
- ☐ Sailboat
- ☐ Schoolbag
- ☐ Screwdriver
- ☐ Squirrel
- ☐ Tennis racket
- ☐ Turtle
- ☐ Worm

How many main rotor blades do most helicopters have?
What gives a helicopter its power?

THIS IS THE LIGHT BEACON.

ROTOR BLADES ARE THE WING-LIKE BLADES THAT SIT ON TOP OF AND ON THE TAIL OF THE HELICOPTER.

LEONARDO DA VINCI DESIGNED A SIMPLE HELICOPTER 500 YEARS AGO.

IGOR SIKORSKY IS CREDITED AS HAVING BUILT THE FIRST SINGLE-ROTOR HELICOPTER THAT SET THE STYLE FOR HELICOPTERS TO COME.

HEAVY DUTY HELICOPTERS CARRY CARGO AND PASSENGERS.

IN 1907, PAUL CORNU, A FRENCH MECHANIC, BUILT THE FIRST HELICOPTER THAT CARRIED A PERSON.

MOST HELICOPTERS HAVE FROM TWO TO SIX MAIN ROTOR BLADES.

HELICOPTERS ARE POWERED BY TURBINE ENGINES.

THE FASTEST HELICOPTERS CAN REACH SPEEDS OF ABOUT 400 MILES PER HOUR.

SOME LARGE HELICOPTERS HAVE TWO MAIN ROTORS THAT SPIN IN OPPOSITE DIRECTIONS. THESE HEAVY DUTY HELICOPTERS DON'T NEED A TAIL ROTOR.

FUEL

THAT'S THE LITTLE HELICOPTER THAT COULD.

I'M DIZZY.

THE SKY IS FALLING!!

I'M A FLYING FISH.

ORCHESTRA

An orchestra is not a random gathering of musicians and their instruments. It is a carefully planned group of different types of instruments with each one having its own part to play in the performance.

See if you can find all the things you did or didn't know about orchestras in this picture. Don't forget to look for the following fun things, too.

- ☐ Ball of string
- ☐ Balloon
- ☐ Baseball cap
- ☐ Bird
- ☐ Broom
- ☐ Brush
- ☐ Candle
- ☐ Cast
- ☐ Duck

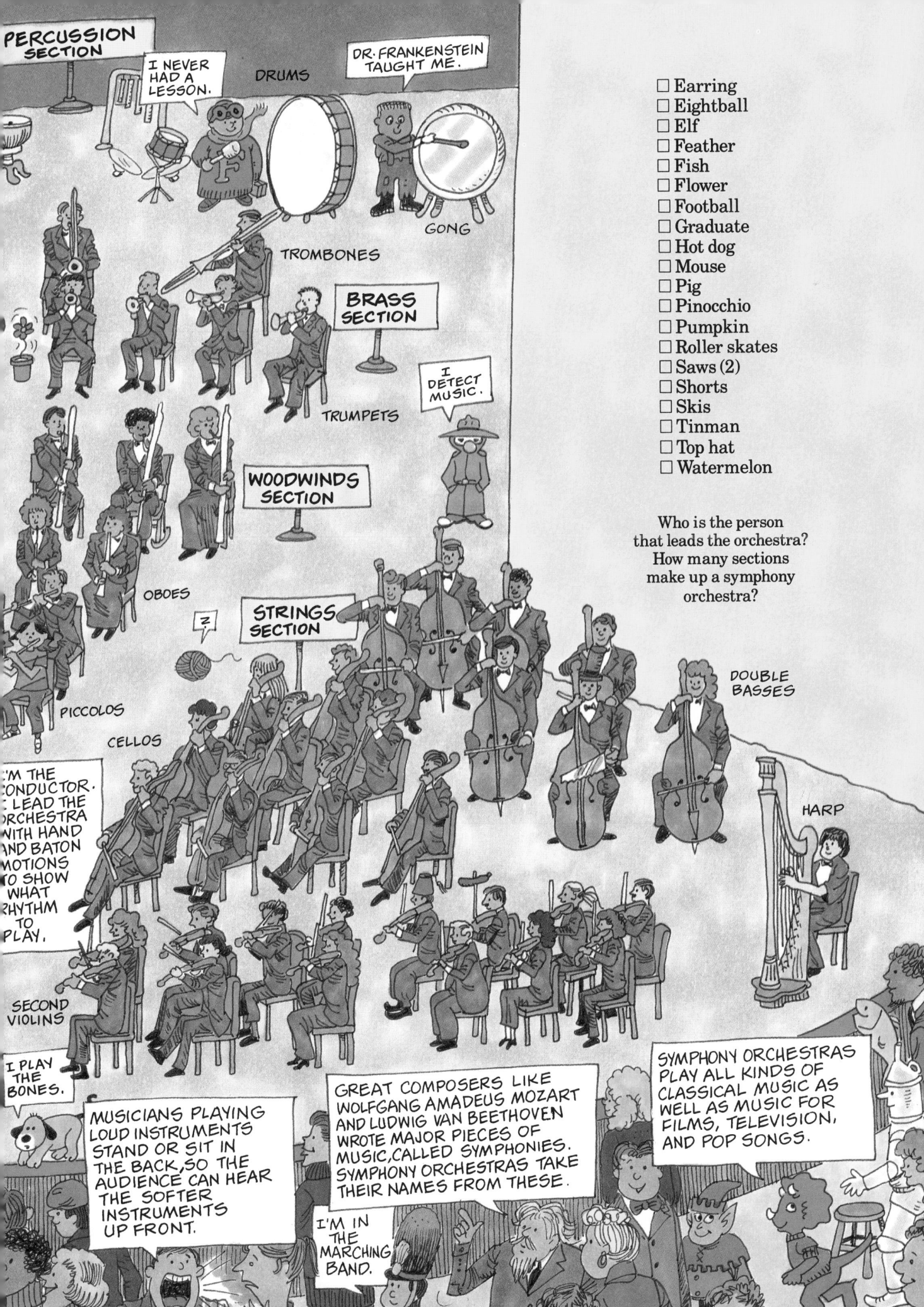

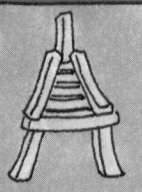
MICROWAVE OVEN

Microwaves are waves of invisible heat energy. Unlike ordinary ovens that use gas or electric heat, a microwave oven uses microwaves to heat, defrost, and cook food.

See if you can find all the things you did or didn't know about microwaves in this picture. Don't forget to look for the following fun things, too.

- ☐ Ball
- ☐ Ballerina
- ☐ Bone
- ☐ Book
- ☐ Bottle
- ☐ Cane
- ☐ Cape
- ☐ Chef's hat
- ☐ Deer
- ☐ Elf

- ☐ Fan
- ☐ Football helmet
- ☐ Fork
- ☐ Hard hat
- ☐ Knife
- ☐ Lion
- ☐ Moose
- ☐ Mouse
- ☐ Napkin holder
- ☐ Necktie

- ☐ Olive
- ☐ Owl
- ☐ Pizza
- ☐ Santa Claus
- ☐ Shark fin
- ☐ Straw
- ☐ Tinman
- ☐ Top hat
- ☐ Turtle
- ☐ Wristwatch

How do microwaves cook food?
Why shouldn't metal containers be used in microwave ovens?

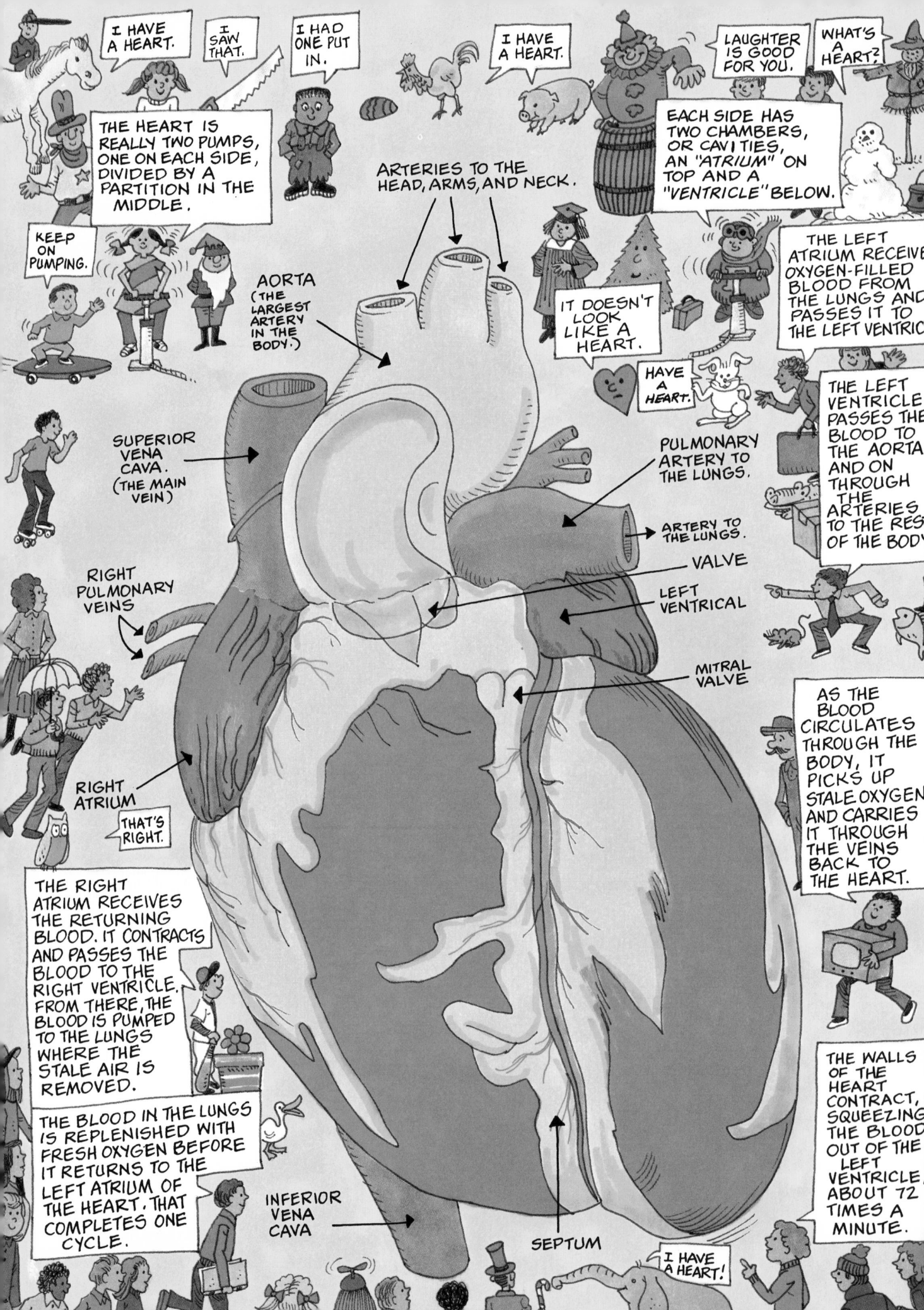

HUMAN HEART

A heart is a muscular pump that circulates blood through the blood vessels. The blood carries nourishment and oxygen to every part of the body. In one year the human heart pumps about 650,000 gallons of blood, enough to fill 50 swimming pools!

See if you can find all the things you did or didn't know about the human heart in this picture. Don't forget to look for the following fun things, too.

- ☐ Ball
- ☐ Banana peel
- ☐ Barrel
- ☐ Baseball bat
- ☐ Book
- ☐ Broom
- ☐ Candy cane
- ☐ Chicken
- ☐ Dracula
- ☐ Drum
- ☐ Duck
- ☐ Fish
- ☐ Flower
- ☐ Joggers (2)
- ☐ Lion
- ☐ Microscope
- ☐ Mouse
- ☐ Moustache
- ☐ Owl
- ☐ Pillow
- ☐ Propeller
- ☐ Roller skates
- ☐ Saw
- ☐ Singer
- ☐ Skateboard
- ☐ Stars (2)
- ☐ Top hat
- ☐ TV set
- ☐ Umbrella
- ☐ Worm

What are the heart's chambers called?

Approximately how long does it take for the blood to travel throughout the body?

EXERCISE IS GOOD FOR YOUR HEALTH.

I HAVE A HEART.

I'M GOING TO OZ TO GET A HEART.

THE HUMAN HEART IS PROTECTED BY THE RIB CAGE IN OUR BODY.

AN ADULT'S HEART IS ABOUT THE SIZE OF A CLENCHED FIST.

IT WEIGHS ABOUT NINE OUNCES.

A DROP OF BLOOD THE SIZE OF THE HEAD OF A PIN HAS ABOUT FIVE MILLION CELLS.

CELLS!

I FEEL LIKE A BLOOD-HOUND.

HEART

RIB CAGE

I LOST MY HEART IN SAN FRANCISCO!

YOU LOST YOUR VOICE THERE, TOO!!

IT HAS A NICE BEAT.

ALIENS HAVE HEARTS, TOO.

IT TAKES ABOUT ONE MINUTE FOR THE BLOOD TO COMPLETE ITS JOURNEY THROUGH THE BODY.

THAT'S FAST!

DIDN'T KNOW THAT!

I KNOW IT NOW!

THE HEART BEAT HAS TWO STAGES. THE ATRIUMS CONTRACT FIRST, FOLLOWED BY THE VENTRICLES. THESE STAGES ARE WHAT CAUSES THE WELL-KNOWN "THUMP-THUMP" SOUND.

THE HEARTBEAT IS AUTOMATICALLY CONTROLLED BY THE NERVOUS SYSTEM. IN-BETWEEN BEATS, THE HEART RESTS.

EACH CHAMBER HAS VALVES THAT CONTROL THE DIRECTION OF BLOOD FLOW THROUGH THE HEART. THEY OPEN AND CLOSE AS THE HEART EXPANDS AND CONTRACTS.

I HAVE A HEART.

DID SOMEONE SAY BLOOD?

AN ADULT'S AVERAGE HEART-BEAT IS 60 TO 70 TIMES A MINUTE.

OUR BODY CONTAINS ABOUT NINE AND ONE HALF PINTS OF BLOOD.

THE BLOOD ENTERS THE ATRIA IN THE UPPER CHAMBERS

THE BLOOD FLOWS THROUGH TO THE VENTRICLES IN THE LOWER CHAMBERS.

THE VENTRICLES RELAX AND FILL WITH BLOOD.

THE VENTRICLES CONTRACT TO PUMP BLOOD INTO THE ARTERIES.

SOLAR ENERGY

Solar energy is power produced by the sun. It can be used to heat and purify water, give power to engines, and produce electricity. Five hundred and fifty billion tons of coal would have to be burned in order to equal the amount of solar energy received by the earth in only one day!

See if you can find all the things you did or didn't know about solar power in this picture. Don't forget to look for the following fun things, too.

- ☐ Apple
- ☐ Arrow
- ☐ Baseball
- ☐ Basketball hoop
- ☐ Bone
- ☐ Brush
- ☐ Buckets (2)
- ☐ Doghouse
- ☐ Duck
- ☐ Earmuffs
- ☐ Fire hydrant
- ☐ Flower
- ☐ Football
- ☐ Ghost
- ☐ Hammer
- ☐ Heart
- ☐ Helmet
- ☐ Kite
- ☐ Mailbox
- ☐ Newspaper
- ☐ Rabbit
- ☐ Screwdriver
- ☐ Star
- ☐ Tepee
- ☐ Turtle
- ☐ Umbrella
- ☐ Umpire
- ☐ Watering can
- ☐ Worm

What is solar power most commonly used for? Why are the insides of solar panels painted black?

AIRPLANE

Airplanes are fascinating pieces of machinery that soar through the air. Whether passenger, private, or military, they all operate under the same aerodynamic principles.

The first power-driven flight was made by the Wright brothers at Kitty Hawk, North Carolina in 1903.

See if you can find all the things you did or didn't know about airplanes in this picture. Don't forget to look for the following fun things, too.

- ☐ "X-1"
- ☐ Acrobat
- ☐ Banana
- ☐ Bowling ball
- ☐ Broom
- ☐ Elephant
- ☐ Fishing pole
- ☐ Flowers (3)
- ☐ Flying carpet
- ☐ Flying horse
- ☐ Flying saucer
- ☐ Football
- ☐ Ghost
- ☐ Glider
- ☐ Hamburger
- ☐ Hang glider
- ☐ Kite
- ☐ Mouse
- ☐ Paper airplane
- ☐ Pencil
- ☐ Pinwheel
- ☐ Pizza
- ☐ Sailboat
- ☐ Seaplane
- ☐ Sled
- ☐ Stars (2)
- ☐ Superheroes (2)
- ☐ Surfboard
- ☐ Turtle
- ☐ Umbrella
- ☐ Yo-yo

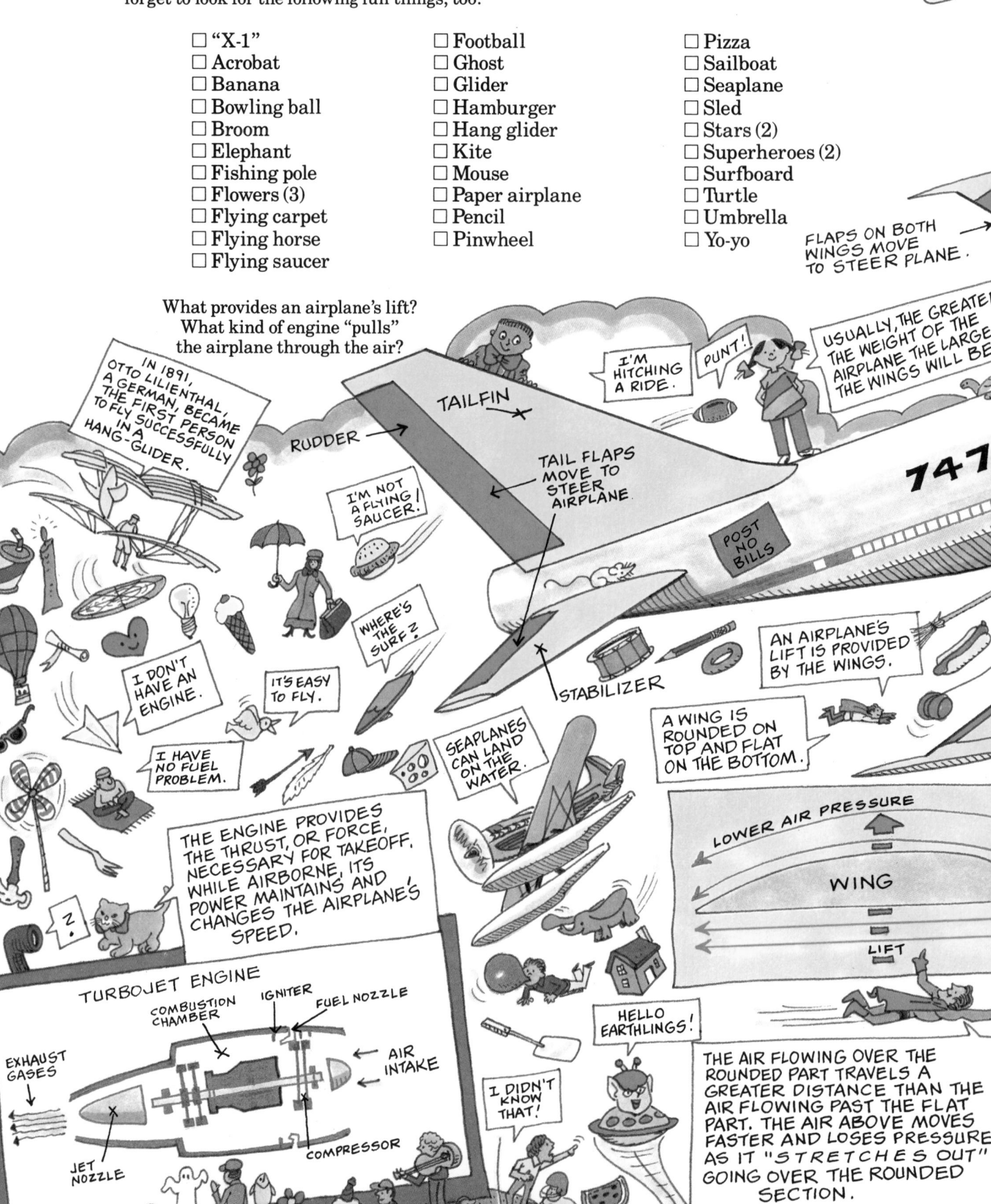

What provides an airplane's lift?
What kind of engine "pulls" the airplane through the air?

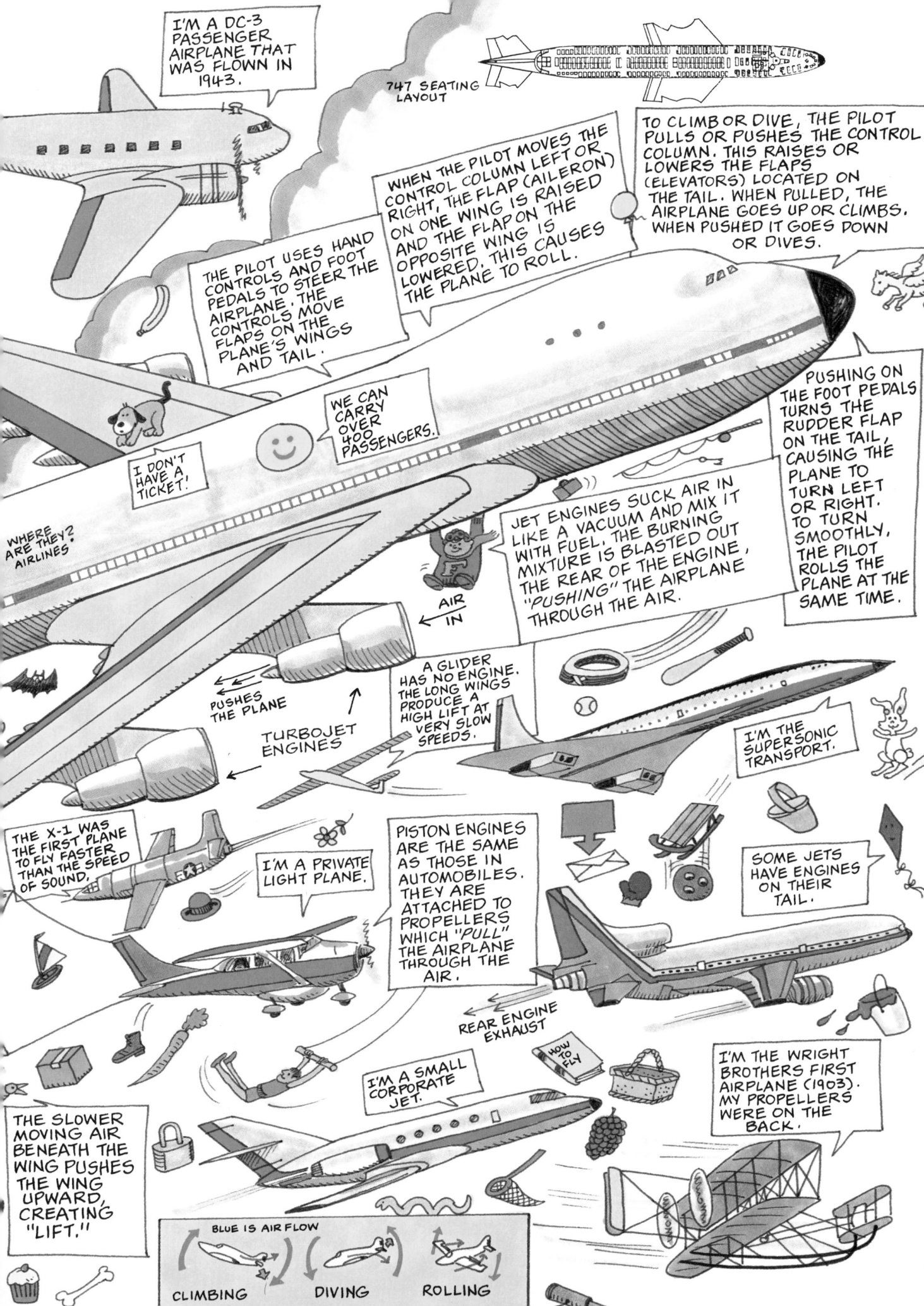

LASERS

A laser is a device that intensifies or increases light. It produces a thin beam of light, stronger than sunlight, that can burn a hole through diamond or steel.

The first operational laser was built in 1960.

See if you can find all the things you did or didn't know about lasers in this picture. Don't forget to look for the following fun things, too.

- ☐ Apple
- ☐ Book
- ☐ Cheerleader
- ☐ Chicken
- ☐ Clock
- ☐ Drum
- ☐ Electrodes (2)
- ☐ Envelope
- ☐ Fish tank
- ☐ Flamingo
- ☐ Football
- ☐ Frog
- ☐ Globe
- ☐ Hot dog
- ☐ Little Red Riding Hood
- ☐ Mouse
- ☐ Necktie
- ☐ Orangutan
- ☐ Painted egg
- ☐ Paper airplane
- ☐ Parrot
- ☐ Roller skates
- ☐ Stapler
- ☐ Stethoscope
- ☐ Straw
- ☐ Thermometer
- ☐ Umbrella
- ☐ Vase

Name two types of lasers.
What are some of the uses of laser beams?

MAGNETS AND MAGNETISM

A magnet is often thought of as a toy that can pull or pick up metal objects. However, the invisible force of magnetism is used in a wide variety of modern devices.

Magnetite, an iron ore containing magnetism, was used as a compass by early sailors to navigate.

See if you can find all the things you did or didn't know about magnets and magnetism in this picture. Don't forget to look for the following fun things, too.

- ☐ Bent nail
- ☐ Bottle cap
- ☐ Cactus
- ☐ Clown
- ☐ Compasses (2)
- ☐ Dart
- ☐ Flower
- ☐ Hard hats (2)
- ☐ Hooks (2)
- ☐ Hot dog

- ☐ Ice-cream cone
- ☐ Kangaroo
- ☐ Key
- ☐ Lion
- ☐ Mermaid
- ☐ Mouse
- ☐ Needle
- ☐ Nuts (2)
- ☐ Paper clips (4)

- ☐ Periscope
- ☐ Pillow
- ☐ Ringmaster
- ☐ Safety pin
- ☐ Shovel
- ☐ Snake
- ☐ Spoon
- ☐ Tinman
- ☐ TV antenna

When is a metal magnetized?
Where are the earth's two magnetic poles?

I'M STAYING RIGHT HERE.

I THINK I'LL PLANT MAGNETS IN MY FIELD NEXT SPRING.

A MAGNETIC FIELD IS THE INVISIBLE FORCE WHICH GIVES THE MAGNET THE ABILITY TO ATTRACT OTHER STEEL OR IRON OBJECTS.

HELP!

I'M FILING A COMPLAINT.

THE MAGNET DOESN'T AFFECT ME!

A BUSY DAY.

ELECTROMAGNETS ARE USED IN ELECTRIC MOTORS.

IN LOUD SPEAKERS.

IN TA AND VIDE RECOR

IN TELEPHONES

ME, TOO!

ME, THREE!

Z

THE MAGNET DIDN'T GET ME YET.

EACH MAGNET HAS A NORTH POLE(N) AND A SOUTH POLE(S).

WHEN THE MAGNETIC FIELDS OF TWO DIFFERENT MAGNETS COME TOGETHER, THEY WILL EITHER REPEL OR ATTRACT.

THE SOUTH POLE OF ONE MAGNET WILL ATTRACT THE NORTH POLE OF ANOTHER MAGNET. IF THE TWO POLES ARE THE SAME, THE MAGNETS WILL REPEL ONE ANOTHER.

A MAGNET CAN STILL RETAIN ITS MAGNETISM IF IT IS CUT IN HALF AS LONG A THE DOMAIN WITHIN EACH PIECE STAY ALIGNED.

N S
S N
S S
N N